DINOSAUR PARADE

Quetzalcoatlus (KWETS-ul-coe-AT-lus)
was a giant flying reptile, not a dinosaur; dinosaurs lived on land, could not fly, and had legs positioned directly under their bodies.

Baryonyx (bah-ree-ON-ix)
used its oversized claws to spear fish.

Coelophysis (SEE-low-FYE-sis)
had hollow bones just like birds that live today.

Stegosaurus (STEG-oh-SORE-us)
had a brain the size of a walnut.

Protoceratops (PRO-toe-SERRA-tops)
roamed the plains in herds.

Dimetrodon (die-MET-roe-don) was a prehistoric reptile but not a dinosaur because of the way its legs were built.

Ankylosaurus (ANK-ill-oh-SORE-us) used its hard, heavy, club-like tail for defense.

Diplodocus (dip-LOD-oh-kus) may have swallowed stones to help it digest food.

Kentrosaurus (KEN-troh-SORE-us) means "spiked lizard."

Gallimimus (GAL-ih-MIME-us) was a fast-moving, bird-like dinosaur.

Elasmosaurus (el-LAZZ-moe-SORE-us) was not a dinosaur but an ocean-dwelling reptile. Dinosaurs lived on land.

For Owen Samuel,
and his dinosaur parades

And for Philemon,
who inspired me to write

ISBN 978-0-545-91789-6

12 11 10 9 8 7 6 5 4 3 2   18 19 20/0

Printed in the U.S.A.   40

First Scholastic printing, October 2015

Designed by Ashley Halsey
Gouache on Bristol board was used to create the illustrations for this book.

DINOSAUR PARADE

Shari Halpern

SCHOLASTIC INC.

Look what's coming!
See what I made!

Down the street—
a Dinosaur Parade!

They come in all sizes.

Coelophysis

They come in all shapes.

Diplodocus

Dimetrodon

Some have clubs.

Ankylosaurus

Others have plates.

Stegosaurus

Some walk on two legs,

Baryonyx

Gallimimus

others on four.

Kentrosaurus

Protoceratops

Elasmosaurus

This one likes water.

This one can soar.

Quetzalcoatlus

Corythosaurus

Here are some plant eaters.

Saltasaurus

Spinosaurus

Allosaurus

These eat meat!

Some look scary.

Tyrannosaurus

Some look sweet.

Maiasaura

Whether they have horns
on their heads,

Triceratops

or a bill like a duck,

Parasaurolophus

whether they are tall,

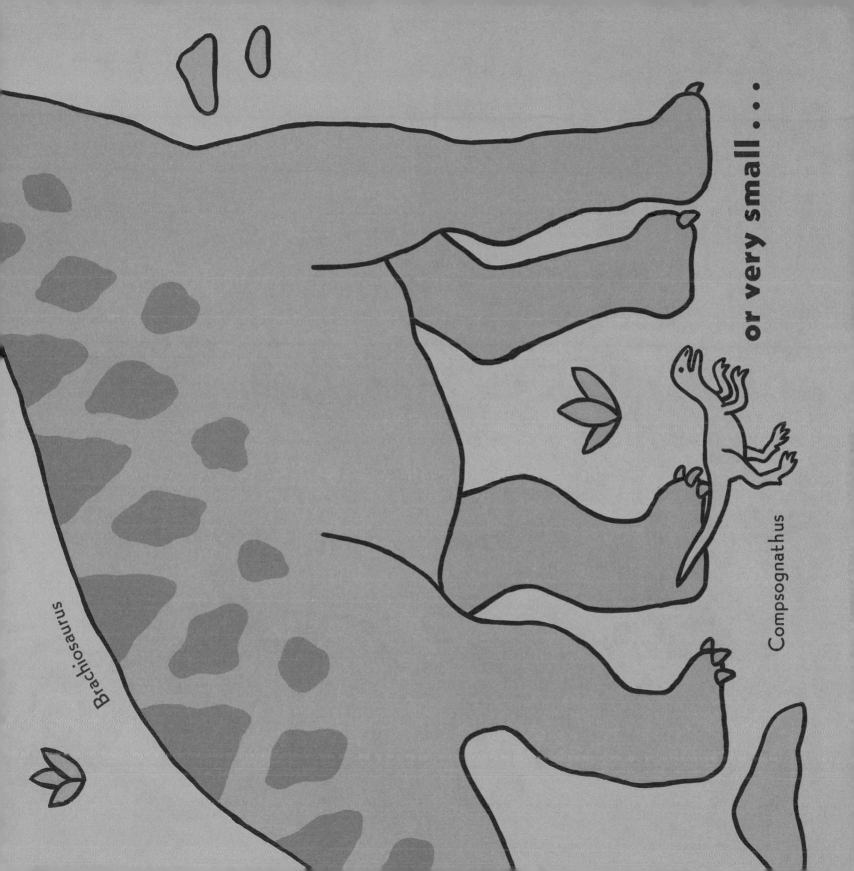

Brachiosaurus

Compsognathus

or very small . . . .

I love them all!
Hooray, DINOSAUR PARADE!

Spinosaurus (SPINE-oh-SORE-us) had a sail on its back and ate fish.

Allosaurus (ah-lo-SORE-us) was fierce, with razor-sharp teeth and claws.

Tyrannosaurus (TIE-ran-oh-SORE-us) had teeth the size of bananas.

Brachiosaurus (brack-ee-oh-SORE-us) lived for about 100 years and had longer front legs than back legs.

Maiasaura (MY-a-SORE-ah) may have nurtured her young babies, unlike most other dinosaurs that let their young fend for themselves.

Compsognathus
(comp-sog-NAITH-us)
was the size of a turkey.

Corythosaurus (ko-RITH-oh-SORE-us)
had a bony crest on the top of its head
and a toothless beak, although it had
sharp teeth in the back of its mouth.

Saltasaurus (SALT-ah-SORE-us)
had bony plates lining its back and had
no toes or claws on its front feet.

Triceratops (try-SERRA-tops)
had three horns on its head.

Parasaurolophus
(PA-ra-SORE-oh-LOAF-us)
was a duck-billed dinosaur that
may have made horn-like sounds.